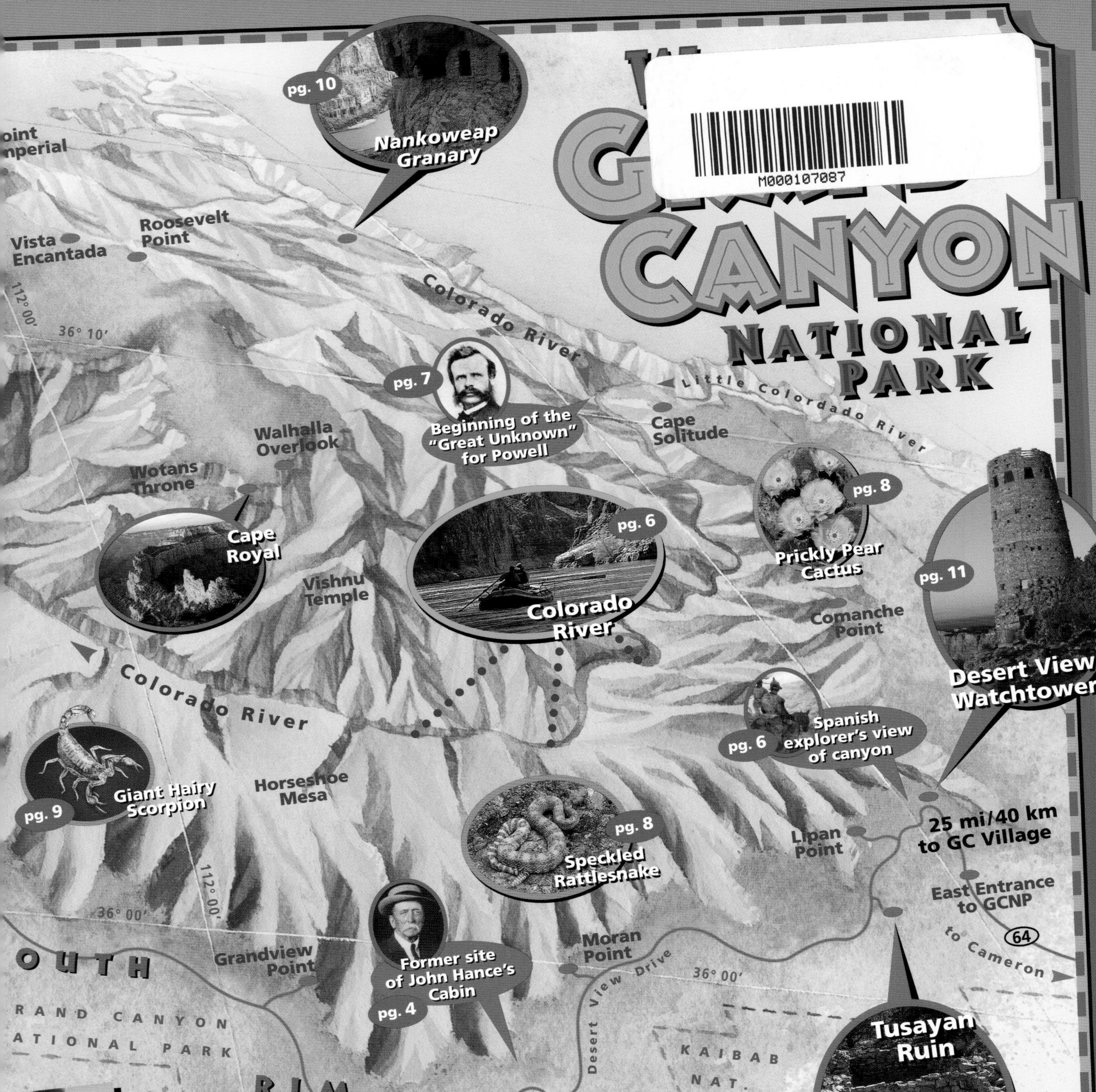

GRAND CANYON NATIONAL PARK

Nankoweap Granary
pg. 10

Point Imperial
Vista Encantada
Roosevelt Point
Colorado River
Beginning of the "Great Unknown" for Powell
pg. 7
Little Colorado River
Cape Solitude
Walhalla Overlook
Wotans Throne
Cape Royal
Colorado River
pg. 6
Vishnu Temple
Prickly Pear Cactus
pg. 8
Comanche Point
Desert View Watchtower
pg. 11
Colorado River
Giant Hairy Scorpion
pg. 9
Horseshoe Mesa
Spanish explorer's view of canyon
pg. 6
Speckled Rattlesnake
pg. 8
Lipan Point
25 mi/40 km to GC Village
East Entrance to GCNP
to Cameron
64
Former site of John Hance's Cabin
pg. 4
Grandview Point
Moran Point
Desert View Drive
South Rim
Grand Canyon National Park
Kaibab Nat. Forest
Tusayan Ruin
pg. 10
64
112° 00′
36° 10′
36° 00′
112° 00′
36° 00′

1901 First train pulls into Grand Canyon Village

1902 Kolb brothers arrive at South Rim

1905 El Tovar Hotel and Hopi House open

1919 Grand Canyon National Park established

1933 Desert View Watchtower completed from Mary Colter design

pg. 11

1979 Grand Canyon designated a World Heritage Site

1996 Captive-bred condors first released near Vermilion Cliffs

2000 Canyon View Information Plaza opens

LINE

Does it SNOW more on the North Rim than South Rim?

Grand Canyon South Rim Weather Records Since 1900

Coldest day
FEBRUARY 7, 1989
12°F/-11°C

Coldest night
FEBRUARY 1, 1985
-20°F/-29°C

Yes! The North Rim gets an average of 150 in/381 cm of snow each winter while the South Rim gets only half that amount!

Why? Because the South Rim is much lower than the North Rim!

The North Rim elevation averages 8,200 ft/2,499 m compared to the South Rim's 7,000 ft/2,134 m.

South Rim temperatures in January average 41°F/5°C high and 18°F/-8°C low.

(The North Rim is closed from mid-October until mid-May.)

KAIBAB
TOROWEAP
COCONINO
HERMIT
SUPAI GROUP
REDWALL LIMESTONE
MUAV LIMESTONE
BRIGHT ANGEL SHALE
TAPEATS SANDSTONE
GRAND CANYO SUPER-GROU

1880'S

Man Walks on FOG at GRAND CANYON

WHEN PEOPLE ASKED ABOUT THE SNOWSHOES LEANING AGAINST PIONEER JOHN HANCE'S CABIN, HE OFTEN TOLD THIS TALL TALE

"One mornin' I woke up and fog had filled the canyon. It was so thick that I decided to put on my snowshoes and walk out a ways. Found out it was thick enough to hold me! So, I started right then to walk out across to the North Rim. And darned if I didn't make it!

Comin' back I ran into a little trouble. See, the fog was gettin' thin here and there and I was startin' to fall through! Thinkin' I better just wait awhile, I set myself down on top of one of them rock temples. And after a few days gone by I lost some weight—enough to continue—and didn't fall through again at all gettin' home!"

THUNDER

Bright Angel Trail

THE AIR TEMPERATURE INCREASES ABOUT 4°F/2.2°C EVERY 1000 FEET OR 300 METERS YOU DESCEND INTO GRAND CANYON!

Hottest day
JUNE 26, 1974
105°F/41°C

Warmest night
JUNE 22, 1973
75°F/24°C

Most rain
MARCH 1, 1970
4 in/24 hours
10 cm/24 hours

July through **September** bring **monsoon storms** to Grand Canyon with *lightning, loud thunder,* and *heavy rains.* July temperatures on the South Rim average 84°F/29°C high and 54°F/12°C low. The inner canyon summer temperatures can reach 115°F/46°C! Always bring water when you hike

How was Grand Canyon made?

KAIBAB LIMESTONE
250 million years ago

TOROWEAP FORMATION
260 million years ago

COCONINO SANDSTONE
270 million years ago

HERMIT SHALE
280 million years ago

SUPAI GROUP
300 million years ago

REDWALL LIMESTONE
330 million years ago

MUAV LIMESTONE
530 million years ago

COLORADO RIVER

BRIGHT ANGEL SHALE
540 million years ago

SHNU
HIST

TAPEATS SANDSTONE
550 million years ago

Layers of time

THE LAND NOW CALLED ARIZONA has changed many times during the past. The scenes you see at left show the *geologic periods,* each of which resulted in a unique layer of stone. *LIMESTONE* came from the skeletons of sea creatures that settled to the ocean floor. Silt and mud in soggy river deltas became *SHALE.* *SANDSTONE* came from vast areas of shifting sand. Over millions of years, each new layer piled on top of the layer below it. *Enormous pressure* caused the materials below to slowly compress into thick layers of stone.

The *Colorado Plateau* is made up of all of these geologic layers. It covers the area where *Utah, Colorado, New Mexico,* and *Arizona* meet and is more than twice the size of New York state! The stone layers here are stacked flat like sheets of plywood.

About *5 to 6 million years* ago the *Colorado River* began cutting down through the layers of the Colorado Plateau like a *saw* cutting through a stack of plywood. The *teeth* of the saw are *sand, gravel, and rocks* carried into the river during spring runoff and intense summer rain storms. *Erosion* occurs when wind, water, or gravity *move* rocks, sand, and soil to new locations.

Uplift of the plateau, like a bulging sidewalk, pushed the *North Rim* higher than the *South Rim.* In the inner gorge the uplift has helped the river cut down to a layer, called *Vishnu Schist,* that is 1.7 billion years old—*nearly half the age of the Earth!*

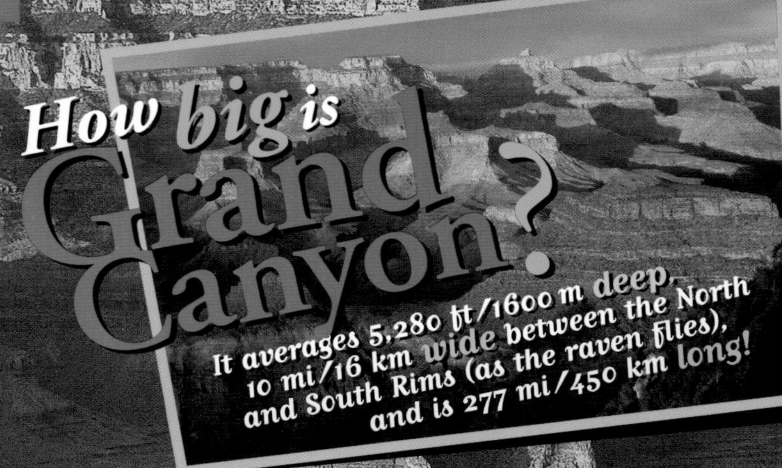

How big is Grand Canyon?

It averages 5,280 ft/1600 m deep, 10 mi/16 km wide between the North and South Rims (as the raven flies), and is 277 mi/450 km long!

What does COLORADO mean in Spanish?

The Colorado River once carried **tons** and **tons** of rusty red sediment suspended in its flow. Seeing the color of the water the Spanish explorers named this *river* of *red* the *Río Colorado.*

In 1963, Glen Canyon Dam was completed 15 mi/24 km **upstream** from Grand Canyon and the dam now traps the **reddish silt.**

The dam also makes the river *very cold* in Grand Canyon. Even during the hot days of summer the water temperature is only about *48°F/9°C. Why?* The water is released from deep below the surface of Lake Powell (the dam's reservoir) where the sun can't reach it.

Who Discovered Grand Canyon?

SPANISH CONQUISTADOR, GARCÍA LÓPEZ DE CÁRDENAS, was mostly interested in finding **gold** or silver when Hopi Indians guided him to the Grand Canyon in 1540. He looked into the canyon somewhere near **Desert View** and was the first person to make a *written* record of it.

But by no means was he the first person to **find** Grand Canyon! Remains of stone dwellings show that **Indians** had built here hundreds of years before he visited. And people hid split-twig figurines *(see page 10)* thousands of years earlier inside **dry caves** in the inner gorge.

WHERE DOES THE COLORADO RIVER BEGIN?

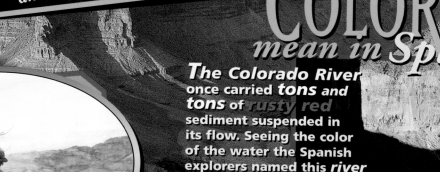

The river begins in the ROCKY MOUNTAIN nearly 2 mi/3 km above sea level in—you guessed it!—the state of Colorado. It drains a area equal to the size of FRANCE! Th original flow led it to th

Name the person who said:

"I want to ask you to do one thing…keep this great wonder of nature as it is….The ages have been at work on it and man can only mar it."

ⓐ John Muir ⓑ John Wesley Powell ⓒ Theodore Roosevelt

See page 15 for the answer.

What was "The Great Unknown"?

MAJOR JOHN WESLEY POWELL led the first river trip through Grand Canyon. He was a self-taught naturalist and geologist from Illinois who lost his right arm fighting in the Civil War! Powell refused to let his disablity hold him back. On May 24, 1869, he launched at Green River, Wyoming with a crew of nine men in four wooden boats *(left)*.

Rowing past the Little Colorado River on the morning of August 10th, the men entered "The Great Unknown"—the last unmapped section of the Colorado River. They spent long, **dangerous** days navigating the deep canyon.

Weeks of **hardship** finally took their toll when three men refused to go any farther and abandoned the trip—as it turned out just before the **last big rapid**. Days later, Powell and his crew emerged from the canyon **victorious**, but the three men were never seen again!

Why does the river have rapids?

White water occurs where large rocks, moved by floods from side canyons, partially dam the river's flow. From Lees Ferry—where Grand Canyon begins—until it ends 277 mi/450 km later at Grand Wash Cliffs, the Colorado River drops about 2,500 ft/760 m and… descends over **160 major rapids!**

Are there Waterfalls in the canyon?

Yes, Grand Canyon has many waterfalls, although most can be seen only by hiking in side canyons. RIBBON FALLS (above) is about 6 mi/10 km up the North Kaibab Trail from Phantom Ranch.

Why are plants at the top and bottom of Grand Canyon different?

● **Hiking down** into Grand Canyon you will see fewer trees and more cactus and lizards. **Why?** Because the **air temperature increases** by about **4°F/2.2°C** for every **1,000 ft/300 m** you **descend.** It is more than **20°F/51°C warmer** at the **bottom** of the canyon than on **the rim.**

● **Slope** and **aspect** also affect where plants and animals can live. Slopes **facing south** get the most sun exposure, making it **hotter** and **drier** than slopes **facing north.** A **hot** environment **decreases** a plant or animal's ability to **retain** its own moisture.

● **Cactus** have adapted ways to **survive** the **heat.** They swell to **store water** after a rain and have a waxy coating to **restrict** moisture loss caused by evaporation.

● **Desert animals** will often **stay hidden** during the day. They will choose, instead, to **hunt** and **forage** at **night** when temperatures are cooler.

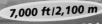

PONDEROSA PINE FOREST

These tall pines grow on both the **North and South Rims.** Small-scal wildfires are good for ponderosa forests. They clean up fallen limbs, dead needles, and cull weak seedlir without harming mature trees wh have thick, protective bark. **Abert and Kaibab squirrels** live in the ponderosa forests (see *page* 9).

4,000-7,500 ft/1,200-2,300 m

PINYON-JUNIPER WOODLAN

Pinyon trees (above) live up to 400 years and junipers survive even longer. Mixed among these 20-30 ft/6-9 m **evergreens** are Mormon tea, fendlerbush, cliffrose, yucca, **agave,** Gambel oak, and sagebrush. **Mule deer** and pinyon jays live in this community.

below 4,000 ft/1,219 m

DESERT SCRUB

The **inner canyon** is mostly a desert community of **cactus** and widely spaced, low bushes. These areas are home to **prickly pear** (left), blackbush, ocotillo, wolfberry, Mormon tea, turpentine brush, and four-wing saltbush. **Rattlesnakes** living here prey on rodents and birds.

Speckled Rattlesnake

Environments such as **Bright Angel Creek** (right), the banks of the Colorado River, and near **seeps, springs,** and **waterfalls** are home to plants that need constant moisture. Golden columbine, maidenhair fern, monkeyflower, and **poison ivy** live in shady, damp places. Redbud, cottonwood, hackberry, and willow grow where the **soil remains moist.**

Are Scorpion Stings Deadly?

YES, BUT usually only to the spiders and small insects they eat.

The last **HUMAN** death in Arizona from a scorpion sting was in 1958.

Venom from the **GIANT HAIRY SCORPION** *(below)* is about as potent as the venom of a honey bee.

The **BARK SCORPION** is smaller but has much more potent venom.

To avoid being **STUNG** don't place your hands in places you can't see—like under a rock or log.

Giant Hairy Scorpion

Do Condors eat other animals?

Yes, but only if they are already DEAD! Scavengers such as condors and vultures eat *carrion*—the DECAYING FLESH of dead animals.

The California condor, the largest flying bird in North America, can get as large as 22 lbs/10 kilos with a wingspan up to 9 ft/3 m.

Condors were becoming EXTINCT when a breeding program was developed to save the species. The first group of captive-bred condors were released near the Vermilion Cliffs (north of Grand Canyon) in 1996.

California Condor

Abert Squirrel

What critter looks different on the South and North Rims?

Grand Canyon's **tassel-eared squirrels** have evolved differently on the South and North Rims. Why? Because the Colorado River divided the territory of their common ancestors a long time ago. They have bred separately ever since. **Abert squirrels** on the South Rim have white bellies and gray tails while **Kaibab squirrels** on the North Rim have dark gray bellies and white tails. **Ponderosa pines** fulfill all the food and shelter needs of both squirrel species.

Collared Lizard

Bighorn Sheep

Mule Deer

Why shouldn't we feed wild animals?

➡**WILD ANIMALS** EAT ANYTHING THAT TASTES GOOD—INCLUDING PLASTIC **FOOD WRAPPERS.** THEIR DIGESTIVE SYSTEMS CAN GET BLOCKED BY THESE PLASTICS CAUSING THE ANIMAL TO BECOME **SICK** FROM **MALNUTRITION.**

BIGHORN SHEEP AND **DEER** CAN BECOME AGGRESSIVE IF THEY FEEL CROWDED BY PEOPLE OR HAVE YOUNG TO PROTECT. VISITORS WHO APPROACH THEM MAY GET **BITTEN, KICKED,** OR **GORED** !

DON'T FEED **SQUIRRELS,** EITHER. **FLEAS** OR **TICKS** ON SQUIRRELS CAN TRANSFER TO YOUR BODY AND SOON MAKE YOU SICK. BESIDES THE HEALTH RISKS, FEEDING GRAND CANYON'S WILD ANIMALS IS **AGAINST THE LAW!**

WHERE CAN I SEE AN ANCIENT INDIAN DWELLING?

SAN FRANCISCO PEAKS
12,633 FT / 3,852 M
SACRED TO HOPI, ZUNI, NAVAJO, AND WHITE MTN. APACHES

DEER HUNTERS

KIVA CEREMONIAL ROOM

CORN DRYING IN THE SUN

DOMESTICATED TURKEYS

GRINDING DRIED CORN INTO FLOUR

WATER CARRIED IN CLAY JARS

12TH CENTURY A.D. 1185

TUSAYAN PUEBLO

is the *easiest* site **to visit.** It is located about **25 mi/40 km** east of **Grand Canyon Village** on **Desert View Drive.**

MUSEUM visitors will **see split-twig figurines, bone tools, stone weapons, decorated pots, kachinas, jewelry,** and **dioramas** while learning about the **Ancestral Puebloan, Hopi, Zuni,** and **Navajo** Indians.

SCHEDULED WALKS are led by **National Park Service rangers** at the **pueblo site.** They talk about how the **ancient Indians** raised and prepared **food,** collected **water,** and kept **warm** during winter.

ANCESTRAL PUEBLOANS began building lasting structures in Grand Canyon and on the canyon rims about A.D. 800. The dwellings made of **stone, mud** mortar, and **timber** roof-beams are called ***pueblos*** (Spanish for *cities*). Small stone and mud enclosures, called ***granaries***, were used to store food reserves (see Nankoweap Granary, page 3).

Indian families cultivated corn and other **crops** and gathered **wild foods** such as cactus fruit, **pinyon nuts**, acorns, mesquite beans, and wild grains. They hunted **bighorn sheep, deer,** and **rabbits,** and raised domesticated **turkeys** for meat. These people eventually moved away from the canyon area by the **middle 1200s.** Why? Probably a period of drought—**lasting two decades!**—made the land too dry to grow their crops. Today, **Hopi** and **Zuni Indians** trace many of their clans back to these **ancient ancestors. Havasupai** *(Hav-a-SU-pi)* and **Hualapai** *(WAL-a-pi)* **Indians** still make their home in Grand Canyon.

21ST CENTURY

Captain Billy Burro, *Havasupai Indian, circa 1900*

Indians used a weapon called the ***atlatl*** (AT-lat-ul) long before they had the bow and arrow. The hooked handle fit into the back of the **spear shaft** making the hunter's throw go farther. These spears had a **sharp stone tip** to kill large animals.

These spear tips are now called ***Folsom points***. In 1993, a broken chip from an ancient Folsom point was found in **Grand Canyon** indicating that Indians have hunted here for at least **10,000 years!**

FOLSOM POINT

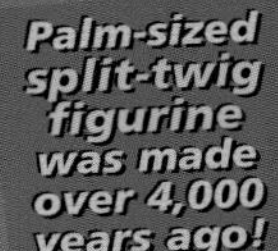

Palm-sized split-twig figurine was made over 4,000 years ago!

Was the DESERT VIEW WATCHTOWER built by ANCIENT INDIANS?

70 ft/21m tall

lo, the tower vas built in 932 from lrawings and a clay model nade by architect Mary Colter. Her nspiration came rom towers she visited at Hovenweep National Monument. Inside he tower is a mural painted by Hopi artist Fred Kabotie. It shows he **LEGEND OF TIYO.** Tiyo was a young Hopi man and is aid to be the very first person to go down the river through Grand Canyon. During his journey Tiyo met and fell in love with a young Indian woman—the daughter of the **SNAKE PRIEST.** Before the Snake Priest would allow Tiyo to marry his daughter he tested Tiyo's courage by surrounding him with hissing **RATTLESNAKES!** Tiyo passed the test and her father approved the marriage. As a gift, Tiyo was taught a ceremony. When Tiyo and his bride returned home he taught it to the Hopi people. The ceremony, called the **SNAKE DANCE,** s still practiced to this day on the Hopi mesas. The ceremony asks for summer rain to come nourish the Hopi corn plants.

Cape Solitude

Comanche Point

Mary Colter

was a designer and architect during the time when most women still didn't work away from the home.

Born on April 4, 1869, in Pittsburgh, Pennsylvania, she graduated from the California School of Design in 1890.

Grand Canyon buildings designed by Mary Colter:

- Hopi House 1905
- Lookout Studio 1914
- Hermits Rest 1914
- Phantom Ranch 1922
- The Watchtower 1932
- Bright Angel Lodge 1935

Grand Canyon PIONEER

THE HERMIT & SILVERBELL

THE HERMIT'S WHITE MULE

By *now, you have* probably heard about the geologic layer **Hermit Shale** (pgs. 4-5) and the stone building at the end of **Hermit Road**, called **Hermits Rest**, where a **hiking trail** leads down to the roaring **Hermit Rapid!**

Who was the hermit?

The "hermit" was Grand Canyon pioneer **Louis Boucher.** After arriving at the canyon, around 1890, he started a **copper mine** and then added some **tourist tents.** He was of **French-Canadian** descent and, among other things, he **loved good food!** So he grew his own **fruits** and **vegetables** and **enjoyed** sharing them with his **guests.** As you can see, **Louis Boucher** wasn't *really* a hermit, he just **enjoyed** being in his **remote canyon**

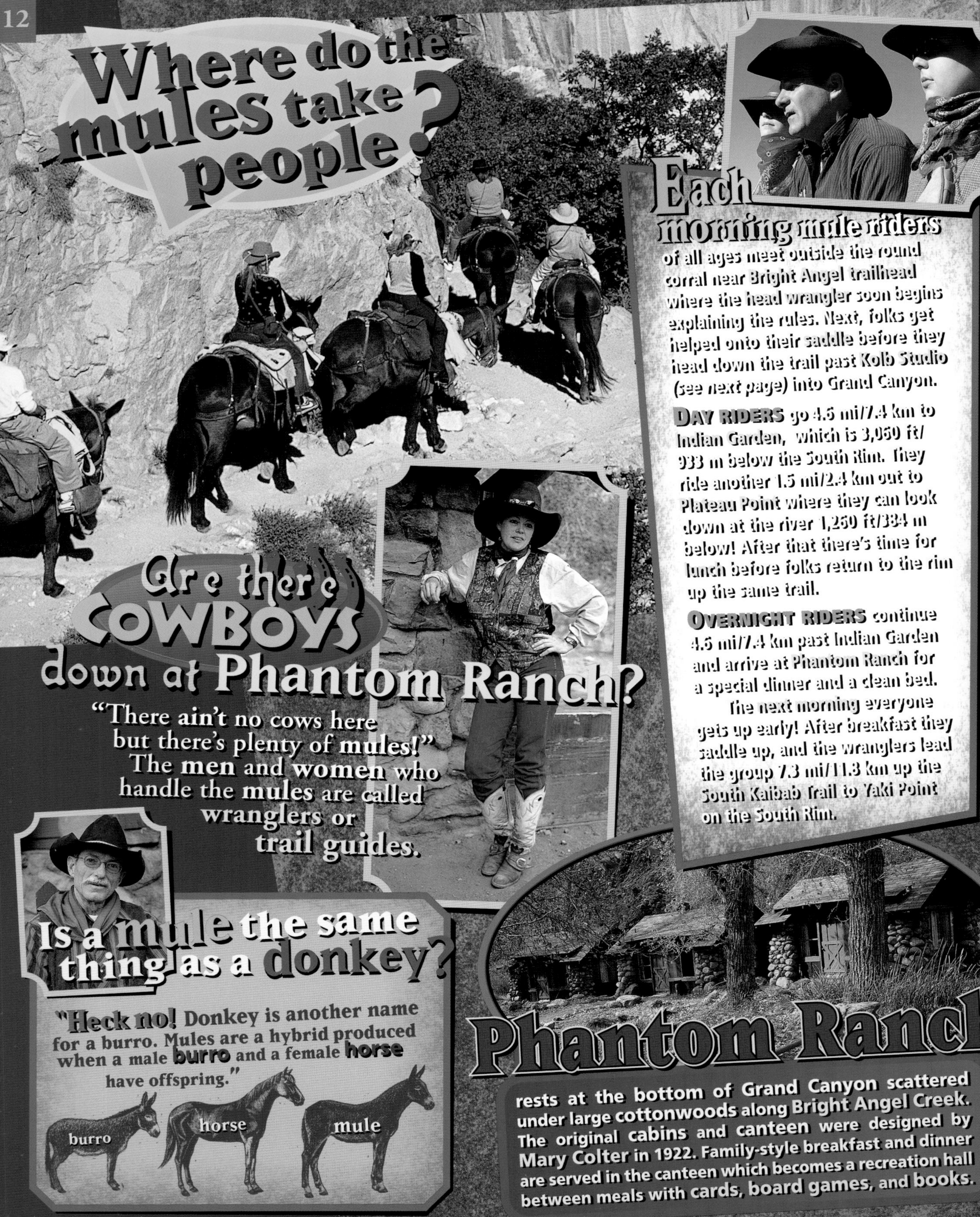

Where do the mules take people?

Each morning mule riders of all ages meet outside the round corral near Bright Angel trailhead where the head wrangler soon begins explaining the rules. Next, folks get helped onto their saddle before they head down the trail past Kolb Studio (see next page) into Grand Canyon.

DAY RIDERS go 4.6 mi/7.4 km to Indian Garden, which is 3,060 ft/ 933 m below the South Rim. They ride another 1.5 mi/2.4 km out to Plateau Point where they can look down at the river 1,260 ft/384 m below! After that there's time for lunch before folks return to the rim up the same trail.

OVERNIGHT RIDERS continue 4.6 mi/7.4 km past Indian Garden and arrive at Phantom Ranch for a special dinner and a clean bed.

The next morning everyone gets up early! After breakfast they saddle up, and the wranglers lead the group 7.3 mi/11.8 km up the South Kaibab Trail to Yaki Point on the South Rim.

Are there COWBOYS down at Phantom Ranch?

"There ain't no cows here but there's plenty of mules!" The men and women who handle the mules are called wranglers or trail guides.

Is a mule the same thing as a donkey?

"**Heck no!** Donkey is another name for a burro. Mules are a hybrid produced when a male **burro** and a female **horse** have offspring."

Phantom Ranch

rests at the bottom of Grand Canyon scattered under large cottonwoods along Bright Angel Creek. The original cabins and canteen were designed by Mary Colter in 1922. Family-style breakfast and dinner are served in the canteen which becomes a recreation hall between meals with cards, board games, and books.

Emery (left) and Ellsworth on the river trip, 1911

The daring Kolb brothers, 1908

DID ARTISTS LIVE IN KOLB STUDIO?

ELLSWORTH and EMERY KOLB were brothers looking for **adventure** when they moved to **Grand Canyon** in 1902. The young men decided to be **photographers** and bought some **used equipment** to get started.

By 1904 they built Kolb Studio *(background photo)* at the **edge of the rim** right above the canyon's main trail. The **mule wranglers** stopped on the trail for group **pictures** and from **inside** the building one of the brothers took the photo **through** an opened window.

Group photo made from Kolb Studio window, 1934

After the **photos** were taken Emery **ran down** the trail to **Indian Garden** (4 mi/6.4 km) to **develop** the film.

Kolb Studio, 1915

He had to use **spring water** there for the **developing process** because the South Rim didn't have **running water yet!** Emery worked quickly, then he **ran back up the trail** so the photos were **ready** and **waiting** for the returning mule riders!

In 1911 the two **daring** brothers made a movie of their river trip on the **dangerous Colorado River** *(top, left)*. The **film** was shown every night, with Emery doing live **narration** at first and later on tape, in the building's downstairs theater. For 64 years straight Emery showed the film and set the **all-time world's record** for the **movie** with the **longest run!**

The **Kolb brothers explored** and made the **first photographs** of many places throughout **Grand Canyon**. Ellsworth eventually moved to **Los Angeles**, but Emery and his wife **Blanche** continued living in the studio and raising their **daughter Edith**. When **Emery** was **93 years old** he took one last trip down the **Colorado River**. He died two years later in 1976.

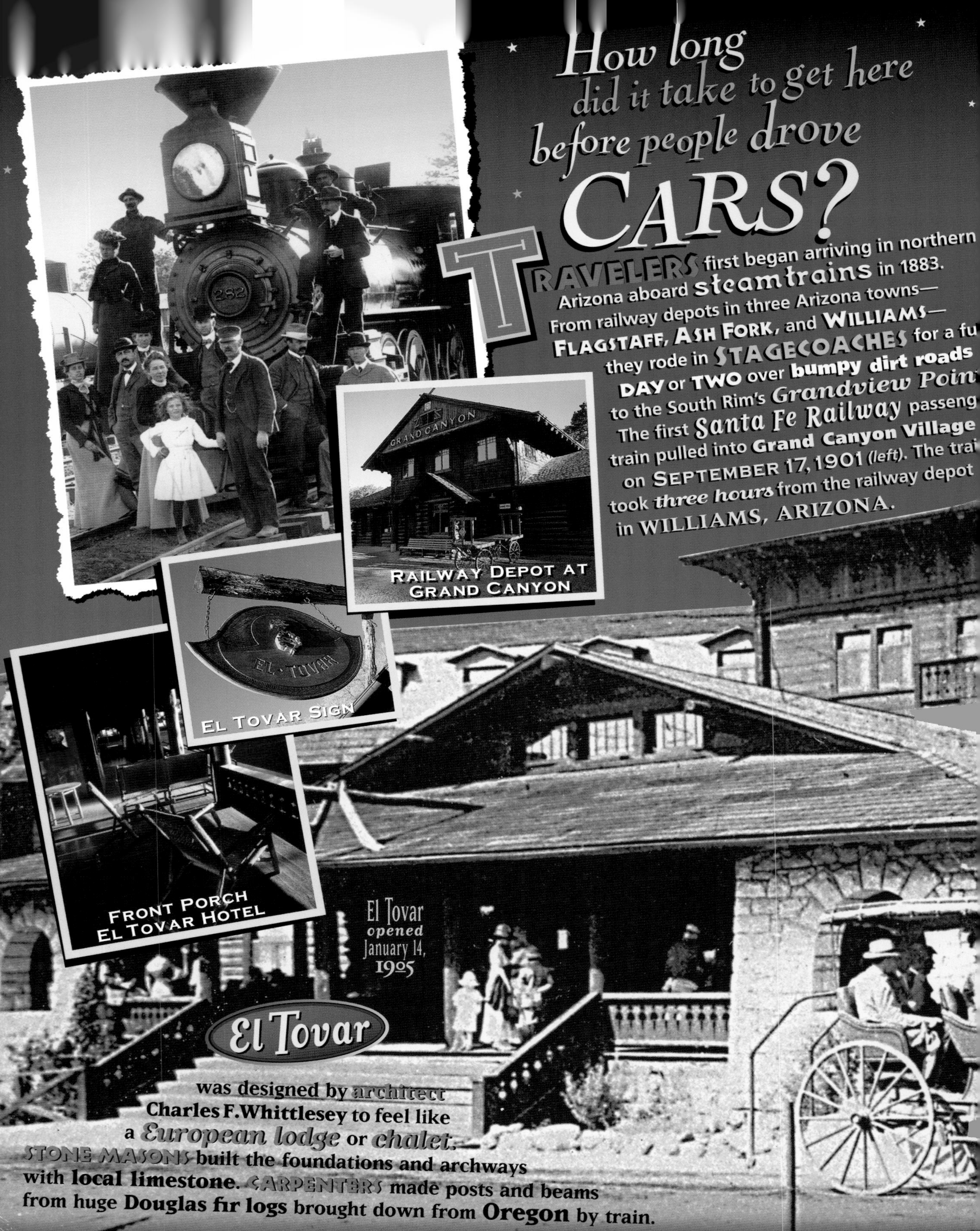
How long did it take to get here before people drove CARS?
TRAVELERS first began arriving in northern Arizona aboard steamtrains in 1883. From railway depots in three Arizona towns—FLAGSTAFF, ASH FORK, and WILLIAMS—they rode in STAGECOACHES for a fu DAY or TWO over bumpy dirt roads to the South Rim's Grandview Poin The first Santa Fe Railway passeng train pulled into Grand Canyon Village on SEPTEMBER 17, 1901 (left). The trai took three hours from the railway depot in WILLIAMS, ARIZONA.
282
GRAND CANYON
RAILWAY DEPOT AT GRAND CANYON
EL TOVAR
EL TOVAR SIGN
FRONT PORCH EL TOVAR HOTEL
El Tovar opened January 14, 1905
El Tovar
was designed by architect Charles F. Whittlesey to feel like a European lodge or chalet.
STONE MASONS built the foundations and archways with local limestone. CARPENTERS made posts and beams from huge Douglas fir logs brought down from Oregon by train.